the Grand National Quiz Book 2003

The Grand National 2003 Quiz Book

ISBN 1-904099-05-X

Printed and bound in Spain by Bookprint SL, Barcelona

First published in 2003 by Garlic Press Publishing Ltd
71 Prenton Road West, Prenton, Birkenhead, CH42 9PZ
Tel: +44 (0)151 608 7006
email: boss@garlicpress.co.uk

www.garlicpress.co.uk

Produced by
Arabella McIntyre-Brown and Guy Woodland

Cover design: Ken Ashcroft
Cover photo: Ron Jones
Proofreader: Debbie Woodland
Additional questions: Tim Martin-Wright
Photography:
Leo Mason and Lisa Linder
John Grossick, Derek Massey
Alan Bannister (Faculty of Veterinary Science, University of Liverpool)

We are most grateful to Martell for permission to use photographs from their collection

Our grateful thanks for enthusiastic help and advice to:
Lew Baxter, Ian Boumphrey, Liz Finch, Jane Hunt, Sue Lydiate, Peter Wicks, Jane Kennedy and Jason Harborow at Re:Activ, and especially to Jane Clarke at the Aintree Museum

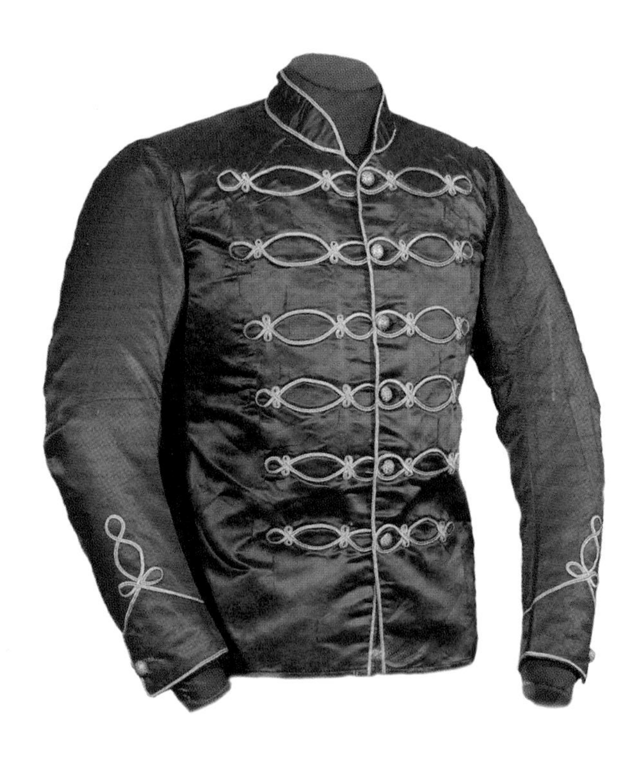

Do you recognise these silks?

FOREWORD

Half a billion people around the globe turn towards Liverpool on one Saturday each Spring, to watch one of the greatest spectacles in sport. Aintree is a magnet for the racing world; the Grand National is one of the most coveted prizes for owners, trainers, and jockeys, and to be on the rails when 100,000 throats roar the name of their fancy is to be part of history, every year.

All the millions of once-a-year punters – who put their shirts (or at least £1 each way) on the prettiest colours, or the horse with the same name as their child's cat – are caught up in the magic along with the racing fraternity.

The Grand National is a dream factory; legends are created in the space of ten minutes and last many lifetimes.

This first-ever Grand National Quiz Book has its own little part of Aintree history, having come to life in something of a race against the clock. From getting the green light on 10th March 2003 to publication on the opening day of the Grand National meeting on 3rd April, this has been the publishing equivalent of the great race: daunting, but what a thrill!

We hope you have fun with this year's quiz: what will you remember for next year's edition?

Arabella McIntyre-Brown and Guy Woodland

21

a. Which is the only horse to have won the Grand National three times?

b. Which horse ran in eight Grand Nationals, won two and ran his last race in 1904 at the age of 16?

c. Having won the National, Mr Frisk completed a big double in 1900 by winning which other famous trophy?

d. Ally Sloper, who won the 1915 Grand National, was named after what?

Jim Culloty winning on which horse in 2002?

a. Which owner of the Waterloo Hotel staged the first Grand National?

b. On what date was the first Grand National run?

c. What does the Saxon name Aintree mean?

d. Which family was associated with the management of Aintree from the 1850s to the 1970s?

PADDY
GRAND
12 BEAU
11 PAPILLON 1
16 EARTHMOVER 2
66 TRESOR DE MAI 3
40 GENERAL WOLFE 5
16 THE LAST FLING 6
HANAKHAM 7
ADDINGTON BOY 8
RED MARAUDER 9
DJEDDAH 10
33 STRONG TEL 11
UNSINKABLE BOXER 12
SUPPORT
STARLIGHT
LORD
HOUSE
1.2.3.4

a. How many adults in the UK have a flutter on the National?

b. What were the lowest odds on a National winner?

c. What do winners Tipperary Tim, Gregalach, Caughoo and Foinavon have in common?

d. How many favourites won the Grand National in the 20th century?

MARTELL
MARTELL
MARTELL
GRAND NATIONAL
AINTREE
RACECOURSE
APRIL 1994
MARTELL
MARTELL CO

a. Which horse won the Grand National on a Monday?

b. Aldaniti beat which horse into second place in 1981?

c. Which horse ridden by Carl Llewellyn won the Grand National in an election year?

d. Rhyme 'n' Reason, who won in 1988, recovered after almost falling at which fence?

Freddie Starr picked up the owner's trophy thanks to this pair: who?

MARTELL

a. Who was the oldest jockey to win the Grand National?

b. In which year did a female jockey first ride in the Grand National?

c. Which champion jockey rode in the Grand National many times but never won it?

d. What was the name of the 51-year old grandmother who finished fifth on Fiddler's Pike, in 1994?

MARTEL
22
CELIBATE
40
33

a. What was the largest number of runners in the National?

b. What is now the maximum number of runners in the race?

c. What was the smallest ever number of runners in the Grand National?

d. In 1928 how many horses finished in the National?

MARTELL
GRAND
NATIONAL

a. Who were the sire and dam of Red Rum?

b. Who were Rough Quest's sire and dam?

c. What do the following stallions have in common: Drayton, Hackler, Jackdaw, My Prince, and Menelek?

d. Which are the only two stallions to sire three Grand National winners?

This one didn't crash! Who was the star of 1996?

a. To stop him slipping in the snow, the 1901 Grand National winner Grudon ran with what stuffed into his horseshoes: sugar, butter, sand?

b. What is Tom Scott, a Liverpool athlete, reputed to have done at Aintree in 1870?

c. Battleship, who won in 1938, was little more than a pony: how high was he?

d. Battleship's jockey, Bruce Hobbs, was the youngest ever to win the National: how old was he?

a. Which is the biggest fence on the course?

b. How did Becher's Brook get its name?

c. The fence at Becher's Brook is how high?

d. When was the fence altered to make it safer?

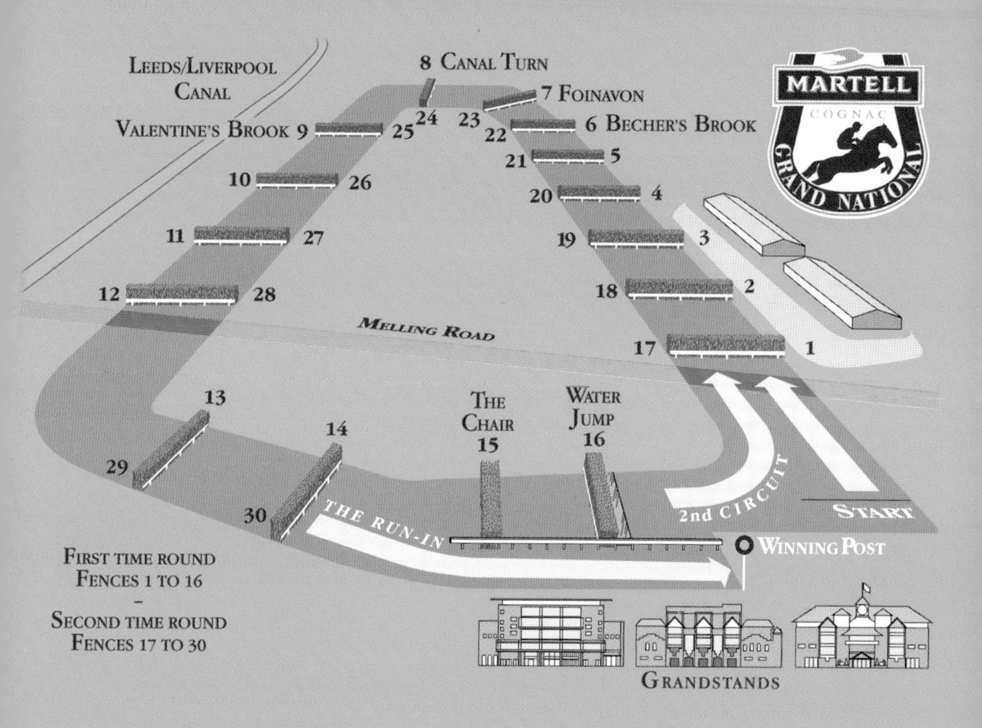
Leeds/Liverpool Canal
8 Canal Turn
7 Foinavon
Valentine's Brook 9
25
24
23
22
6 Becher's Brook
21
5
10
26
20
4
11
27
19
3
12
28
18
2
Melling Road
17
1
13
The Chair 15
Water Jump 16
14
29
30
The Run-In
2nd Circuit
Start
Winning Post
First time round Fences 1 to 16
–
Second time round Fences 17 to 30
Grandstands
Martell
Cognac
Grand National

a. Which Scottish mountain won the Grand National in 1980?

b. What was unusual about Esha Ness coming first in 1993?

c. Who beat Red Rum in the 1975 Grand National?

d. Rubio (the first American-bred horse to win the Grand National) at one time pulled what vehicle?

a. Aintree Racecourse is six miles to the north of which city centre?

b. Which canal runs past Aintree and gives Canal Turn its name?

c. The runners cross a road four times on the National course: where does it lead?

d. What postcode area is Aintree Racecourse in?

...[whipped round start and took no part once in 1983/4] and tends to hang under pressure on occasions: seemed unsuited by sharp course at Stratford on fourth start 1986/7. MISS A. L. M. KING **153**
10-0 (9-7)
White, royal blue star, royal blue and white check cap. (Queensway Securities Limited)

BEAMWAM 11 br.g. Bing II–Camute Lady (Hardicanute) [1987/8 c20s^{2} c28s* c24g* c26d^{5} c22g^{3} :: 1988/9 c24d c24d^{3} c26s^{bd} Mar 9] tall, close-coupled gelding: very useful hunter chaser: wide-margin winner at Southwell and Nottingham last season: has dropped out in latter stages having made rapid headway in middle part of race both completed outings this term, but gave indications that he retains most of his ability when 12 lengths third to Risk A Bet at Nottingham in February: has won over 3¼m, but is probably better at slightly shorter distances and is effective at 2m: acts on any going. O. SHERWOOD **170**
10-0 (9-7)
Dark blue and black check, quartered cap. (Mr D. Naylor-Leyland)

LITTLE POLVEIR 12 b.g. Cantab–Blue Speedwell (Escart III) [1987/8 c26s^{2} c29s* c30v^{ur} c28s* c30v c28s^{3} c24s^{5} c36d^{ur} c33s^{pu} :: 1988/9 c26g* c29g^{5} c28s^{3} c32s^{4} c30s c28s^{3} c24v^{5} c25d^{4} Mar 10] strong, lengthy gelding: useful chaser: won minor event at Fontwell in October: in frame in handicaps at Haydock (2) and Bangor since: spoilt his chance with a couple of mistakes when over 20 lengths third to Rausal on last-named course: ran in snatches fifth start: very well suited by a test of stamina (in lead and still travelling strongly when unseating rider 5 out in Seagram Grand National at Liverpool last season): best on an easy surface: suited by forcing tactics and strong handling (has run moderately in amateur riders events last 2 starts): inclined to make the odd mistake: trained until after seventh outing by J. Edwards. G. B. BALDING **158**
10-0 (9-7)
Saxe blue, black stripe on cap, scarlet sleeves. (Mr Edward Harvey)

SERGEANT SPRITE 9 gr.g. General Ironside–Miss Sprite (Bowsprit) [1987/8 c20g^{2} c16v* c20d^{3} c20s^{2} c18v* c16s^{2} c28g :: 1988/9 20f c17d^{2} c16d^{3} c20d^{6} c24v^{2} c24g* c24s^{3} c24s c24d^{3} c24d^{F} c20s^{2} Mar 1] ex-Irish gelding: winning hurdler: fair handicapper over fences: claimer ridden when winning at Fairyhouse in November: placed on same course (twice) and at Leopardstown since, at Leopardstown 4 lengths second to Old Court: stays 3m: seems to act on any going: trained until after latest start by A. Moore. P. RANSOM **161**
10-0 (9-5)
Red, royal blue triple diamond, white sleeves, red and royal blue quartered cap. (Mr David Worth)

BARTRES 10 ch.g. Le Bavard (FR)–Gail Borden (Blue Chariot) [1987/8 NR :: 1988/9 c20d^{3} c20s^{3} c20d^{4} c21g* c24s* c20d Mar 15] lengthy, plain, raw-boned ex-Irish gelding: carries little condition: useful chaser: jumped well in main when winning minor event at Wincanton (by 7 lengths from Paddyboro) and Fairlawne Chase at Windsor in February: jumped badly left last but soon quickened clear when beating Arctic Stream 6 lengths in slowly-run race over 3m on latter course: bandaged all round, jumped none too fluently and was struggling a long way out in handicap at Cheltenham latest start: acts on any going: usually held up: has shown a tendency to hang under pressure and has worn blinkers (not this season). D. J. G. MURRAY-SMITH **173**
10-0 (9-3)
Emerald green, red diamond and diamond on cap. (Mrs David Buik)

MR BAKER 11 ch.g. Fulvous–Clonaghadoo (Perspex) [1987/8 c20m^{3} c22f^{3} c18f^{3} c20m^{4} c20g^{6} c24v* c19v^{2} 20v^{6} c22v^{2} c25v 22v c26v^{3} 24d c24s^{6} c22g^{6} :: 1988/9 c20m^{4} c22s c21g c22d^{4} c22v* c26v Feb 25] strong, workmanlike gelding: handicap hurdler/chaser: having first race since August when winning 8-runner event over fences at Tramore in January by 8 lengths from Navallus VI: well beaten in valuable event won by same horse at Punchestown following month: probably stays 27f: probably acts on any going: blinkered fourth start... season. R. J. WHITFORD, IRELAND **148**
10-0 (8-13)
Emerald green, royal blue stars...

TEAM CH...

a. The music that introduces the BBC's Grand National coverage each year comes from which film sound-track?

b. Which year did the BBC first broadcast the National on television?

c. Who was the commentator on the first televised National?

d. Which was BBC commentator Sir Peter O'Sullevan's last Grand National?

Peter O'Sullevan's notes, now in the Aintree Museum

a. In which year did Red Rum first win the Grand National?

b. On what surface did Red Rum famously have his training gallops?

c. Which Australian horse was many lengths ahead before being caught by Red Rum at the Elbow in 1973?

d. In which two years did Red Rum come second in the Grand National?

Famous colours worn for three National victories

MARTELL
GRAND NATIONAL

a. Who was the first woman to train a Grand National winner?

b. Who trained Red Rum?

c. Which father and son team trained and rode the National winner in 2000?

d. Who is the most recent permit holder (amateur trainer) to have trained a National winner?

MARTELL
GRAND NATIONAL
MARTELL
GRAND
NATIONAL
MARTELL

a. The Queen Mother's horse in 1956 was most famous for not winning: his name?

b. Who was the first horse (who ran in 1894) officially owned by the Prince of Wales?

c. What happened to Ambush II's royal owner between his 1900 National win and his next attempt in 1903?

d. The Queen Mother's first runner in the National was Monaveen in 1950: where did he come?

What sort of 'royal' is this winner from 1995?

SENSATION

a. Bob Champion beat which illness to win the 1981 Grand National on Aldaniti?

b. From what did Aldaniti recover to win the 1981 Grand National?

c. In 1977, after two wins and two second places, Red Rum made history with his third win: who did he beat and by how many lengths?

d. Who fell off Conrad into a brook in the very first National?

a. Why was the 1993 National declared void?

b. How many horses completed the course in the National that Never Was?

c. Which horse finished first in the National That Never Was?

d. Which jockey got tangled up in the starting tape and caused the second false start in 1993?

Seagram
NATIONAL

a. Which holiday tycoon owned 1971 winner Specify?

b. Who owned legendary winner Aldaniti?

c. Which American film star owned Owen's Sedge (1963) and Different Class (1968)?

d. Who owned Red Rum?

Anne, Duchess of Westminster, suspected she might win: with which horse?

11
AGRAM

a. Glenside, the 1911 Grand National winner, had only one what?

b. How many horses have won the Grand National twice?

c. Golden Miller won the Grand National in which year of the 1930s?

d. Which trophy did Golden Miller win for five consecutive years?

Which jockey is enjoying the view from the saddle of his 1991 winner?

a. What was the 1944 film about a girl winning the Grand National?

b. Which winning team was the subject of the 1983 film *Champions*?

c. Who played the lead role in *Champions*?

d. Who directed *Champions*?

Who's this film star with Kilmore?

a. Which famous painter of racehorses such as Whistlejacket and Molly Longlegs was born and worked in Liverpool?

b. To celebrate which monarch's coronation were horses raced in Liverpool in 1558?

c. Which other world-famous horse race has its origins in Liverpool?

d. Which is Britain's fourth largest bookmaker, based in Liverpool?

a. Who is the most recent amateur jockey to win the National?

b. Richard Pitman and son Mark have what galling National result in common?

c. Who is the only jockey to have won the Grand National in both the 1980s and 1990s?

d. The jockey who famously didn't win in 1956 became a best-selling author: who was he?

a. Which jockey announced his retirement a couple of years before winning the National in the 21st century?

b. Who was the aptly-named jockey who won the Grand National on a Monday?

c. Who was the first woman to complete the Grand National course?

d. In the late 1800s four brothers (Tommy, Harry, Willie & Johnny) rode four winners, six seconds and two thirds in the National: what was their surname?

a. In which month is Ladies' Night held at Aintree?

b. In which year was the National moved to a Saturday?

c. When was the first November meeting at Aintree?

d. How many races are there on Grand National Saturday?

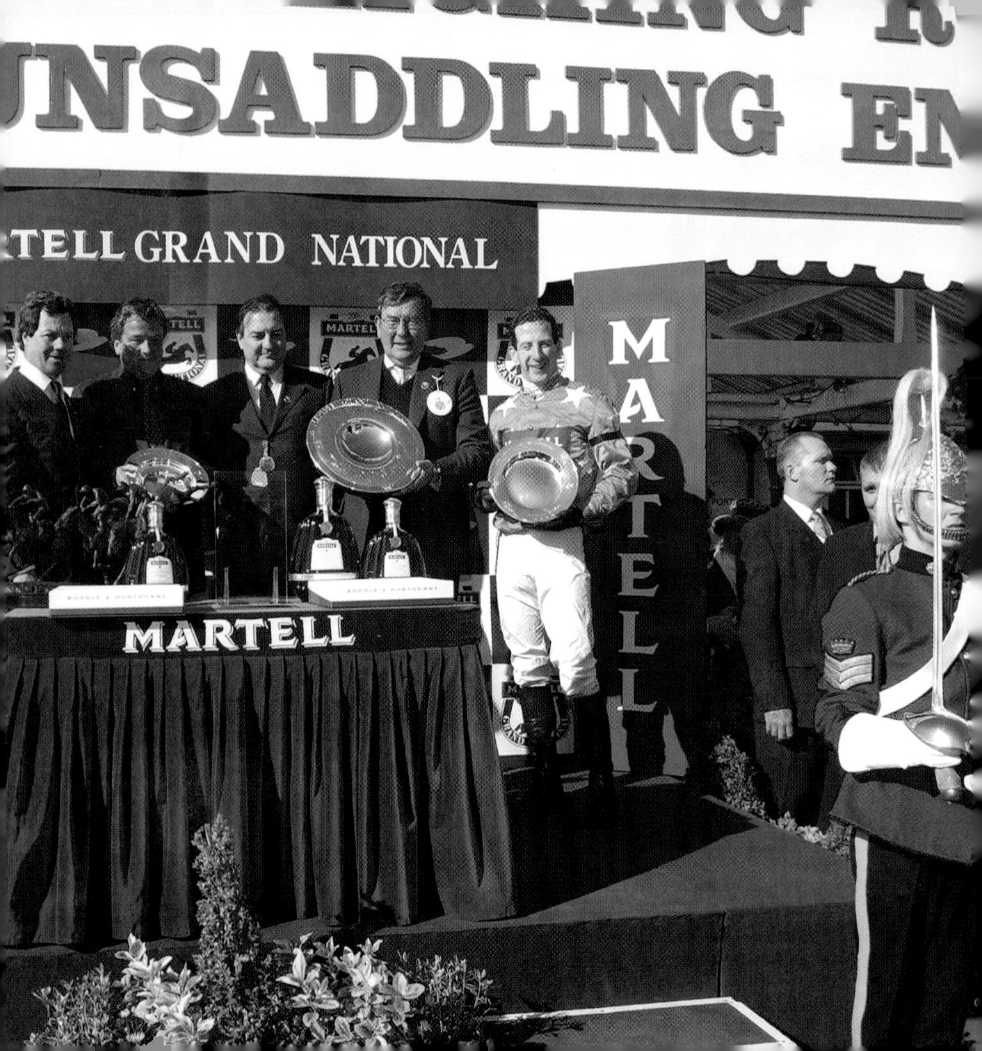

NSADDLING E
TELL GRAND NATIONAL
MARTELL
MARTELL

a. In World War II (1941-1945), what was Aintree Racecourse used for?

b. Which aristocrat. nicknamed Lord Dashalong, leased land to William Lynn on which to build the steeplechase course?

c. Who is the current chairman of Aintree Racecourse (pictured, far left)?

d. From 1916 to 1918, because of World War I, where was the substitute Grand National held?

Presenting the trophies to the Bindaree team in 2002

MARTELL COGNAC
MARTELL COGNAC
MARTELL COGNAC
MARTELL COGNAC
MARTELL COGNAC
1
13

a. Which famous trainer had a success with Miinnehoma in 1994?

b. Vincent O'Brien had how many National wins in a row in the 1950s?

c. Josh Gifford bought which National legend at the Ascot sale in 1974?

d. What was 'Ginger' McCain's proper first name?

a. What physical handicap did Charles Boyce overcome to ride Emigrant to victory in 1858?

b. In 1928, most of the field dropped out when Easter Hero fell at which fence?

c. In 1967, Popham Down ran right across which fence to cause complete chaos?

d. In 2001, only four horses finished after loose horse Paddy's Return trotted across which fence?

21

a. How many fences are jumped in the Grand National?

b. Which two fences are jumped only once in the Grand National?

c. How long is the Grand National course?

d. What is the feature that runners negotiate after the last fence?

Mely Moss (right) pursued by Bindaree and the rest of the field

a. Which past winner is Fence 7 named after?

b. Which feature makes the Canal Turn famous?

c. Which feature do the runners cross for the second time between Fences 12 and 13?

d. What sort of fence is Number 16?

a. Valentine, the horse that gave his name to Valentine's Brook, won the 1840 Grand National: true or false?

b. What is the official height of the first fence on the National course?

c. What material is used to build the Grand National fences?

d. Which fence on the first circuit becomes the last fence on the second circuit?

a. Rummy completed his first win in a record time: nine minutes and how many seconds?

b. In which year did Red Rum die?

c. How old was Red Rum when he died?

d. Where is Red Rum buried?

Which former jockey sculpted Red Rum's statue?

MARTELL
AINTREE
RACECOURSE
1998

a. Which 1970s winner won the National in two different counties?

b. Which horse won the first Grand National?

c. Which National winner had the longest name?

d. Which two National winners had the shortest names?

What was the starting price for Earth Summit in 1998?

a. Which is the newest building for spectators, opened in 1998?

b. Which stand was opened in 1991?

c. The Aintree Mound viewing area overlooks which fence?

d. Which are the two viewing areas named after 1980s winners?

Which Asian racecourse hosted this Martell Grand National event in 2001?

Seagram
6

a. Which horse holds the record for the fastest finishing time?

b. Which was the first horse to win the Grand National in under 10 minutes?

c. What is the fastest winning time for the Grand National to date?

d. What was the course record set by Reynoldstown in the 1935 Grand National?

Who was on board this record-breaker in 1990?

The Seagram Grand National

PRIZES

a. The Grand National Perpetual Trophy depicts what?

b. In 2002 what was the minimum guaranteed prize money in the Martell Grand National?

c. Which Liverpool jeweller makes the current Martell Grand National Winners' Trophy?

d. In 1903, what was the prize money won by Drumcree's owner, Mr H Morrison?

These horses are caught in bronze, landing over which fence?

Valentine's Brook by Edward Benjamin (1885)

RED RUM
3RD MAY 1965
18TH OCTOBER 1995
Grand National Record
1973 - Winner
1974 - Winner
1975 - Second
1976 - Second
1977 - Winner
RESPECT THIS PLACE,
THIS HALLOWED GROUND
A LEGEND HERE
HIS REST HAS FOUND
HIS FEET WOULD FLY,
OUR SPIRITS SOAR
HE EARNED OUR LOVE
FOR EVERMORE

a. Where was Red Rum trained?

b. When was Red Rum's second win at the Grand National?

c. Name Red Rum's two winning Grand National jockeys?

d. Which favourite fell at Becher's in 1977 to leave Red Rum to his third victory?

a. In 1885, what kind of foul play was suspected?

b. On what day of the week was the 1997 National run?

c. Why was the 1997 Grand National postponed?

d. In the largest evacuation in Britain since 1945, how many people left Aintree on race day 1977?

Who had to stay when Aintree was evacuated in 1977?

G. C
Perrin
Segonza

a. Why were race sponsors Seagram celebrating more than usual at the end of the 1991 Grand National?

b. Who first sponsored the Grand National in 1992?

c. In which year was Martell's cognac house founded?

d. Who were the new sponsors of the National in 1975?

Martell cognac is aged in small handmade barrels made of what wood?

TREE
GRAPHER

a. Which 1980s Aintree legend completed a charity walk from London to Liverpool?

b. Which horse won the Grand National in 1935 and 1936?

c. Which is the only horse to win Grand National Races in two different locations?

d. How many National winners' names have included 'Red'?

Who's the gem who won in millennium year?

a. Which is the only owners' syndicate to have a National winner?

b. Who owned the 2002 winner Bindaree?

c. Who is the only man to own three different National winners (1873, 1874, 1876)?

d. Who has been the only royal owner of a Grand National winner?

Congratulations for Raymond Mould in 2002

a. In which year did the BBC first broadcast the Grand National on radio?

b. When was the Grand National first broadcast live on Chinese national TV?

c. In 1992, 40 countries broadcast the Grand National; how many countries took the live broadcast in 2001?

d. What was the worldwide television audience for the 2001 Grand National?

The Princess Royal with the BBC's 'voice of the Grand National' – his name?

a. What kind of race is the Grand National?

b. How old must horses be to run in the Grand National?

c. What is the name of the Czech equivalent of the Grand National steeplechase?

d. Who is the only man to have ridden a Grand National winner and started a Grand National?

a. How is the Grand National started?

b. In which year was the Grand National first run as a handicap?

c. Four horses won with top weight (12-7): Cloister, Jerry M, Poethlyn, and which other?

d. Freetrader won in 1856 with the lightest weight: what?

Not all horses exercising on Merseyside beaches are potential Red Rums...

MARTELL

a. How many spectators come to Aintree for Grand National day each year?

b. Grand National spectators can watch races from which Far East racecourse on Aintree's giant TV screens?

c. How many people came to watch the live broadcast of the Grand National in Hong Kong in 2001?

d. In which year did Concorde land at Liverpool Airport, full of Grand National racegoers?

MARTELL
MARTELL
AINTREE
RACECOURSE
10

a. What put Charity, winner of the 1841 Grand National, into the record books?

b. The Lamb, twice Grand National winner in 1868 and 1871, had what physical distinction?

c. Which double National winner also came third three times and fourth once?

d. The skeleton of the 1897 and 1899 Grand National winner stands in which veterinary school?

a. In the 1857 Grand National, how many false starts were there?

b. In 1956, which horse fell without apparent reason, yards from the finishing post?

c. Which horse was walked all the way from his stables near Grimsby to Liverpool and back to win the 1845 Grand National?

d. Tim Brookshaw riding Wyndburgh to second place in 1959 was an heroic feat: why?

Gerry Scott did the unique double of winning and starting the National

WEIGHING
UNSADDLING
THE MARTELL GRAND NATIONAL
MARTELL

a. Which jockey rode Esha Ness to a false victory in 1981?

b. How many times did Lester Piggott win the Grand National?

c. Lester Piggott's grandfather Ernie Piggott won the National three times – on which horses?

d. George Stevens, the top Grand National winner, won how many times?

a. Who starred as Velvet in the 1944 film *National Velvet*?

b. What was the name of Velvet's horse in *National Velvet*?

c. What was the result of the race in *National Velvet*?

d. Who was the female star of the 1978 sequel, *International Velvet*?

THE MARTELL GRAND

a. Which National winning horse appeared on the stage at Drury Lane in the 1880s after he retired?

b. Party Politics won in 1992 in heroic style: what physical handicap did he have?

c. Who was the second and most recent grey to win the National?

d. The Lamb's two victories in 1868 and 1871 sandwiched which other horse's double win in 1869/1970?

A happy Jim Culloty with the 2002 trophy

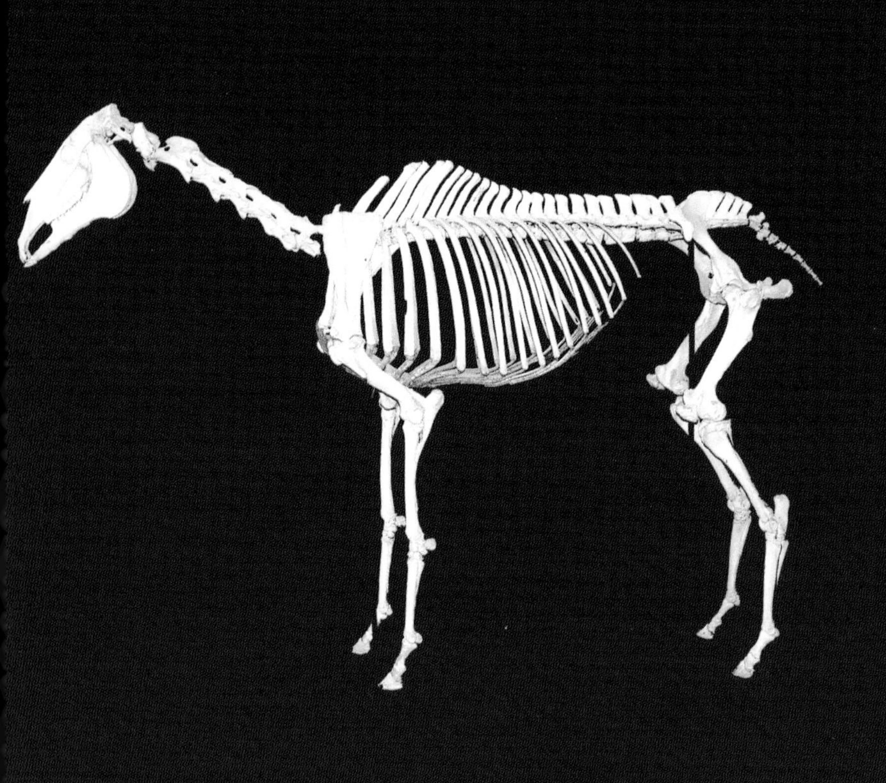

a. Which three former winners were declared for the 2003 Grand National?

b. How many horses were declared for the 2003 Grand National in February?

c. Which day does the Martell Grand National meeting begin in 2003?

d. On what date and time is the 2003 Martell Grand National?

Page 4 – pic: if you know the answer then send an email to boss@garlicpress.co.uk (first 5 correct winners will receive a copy of 'Cross the Mersey')

Page 7 – WINNERS

a. Red Rum **b**. Manifesto **c**. Whitbread Gold Cup **d.** A newspaper cartoon character

Page 9 – AINTREE

a. William Lynn **b.** Tuesday 26th February 1839 **c**. 'One tree' or 'tree standing alone' **d.** The Topham family

Page 11 – BETTING

a. 15 million **b.** 11-4 (Poethlyn, 1919) **c.** They won the National at odds of 100-1 **d.** Eleven (Earth Summit was the last, in 1998)

Page 13 – WINNERS

a. Lord Gyllene **b.** Spartan Missile **c**. Party Politics **d.** Becher's Brook **pic**: Richard Dunwoody on Miinehoma

Page 17 – JOCKEYS

a. Dick Saunders, aged 48 (Grittar, 1982) **b**. 1977 (Charlotte Brew on Barony Fort) **c.** Peter Scudamore **d.** Rosemary Henderson

Page 19 – THE FIELD

a. Sixty-six (in 1929) **b**. Forty **c.** Ten **d.** Two

Page 21 – BREEDING

a. Quorum and Mared **b.** Crash Course and Our Quest **c**. They all sired two separate Grand National winners **d.** Cottage (Workman, Lovely Cottage, Sheila's Cottage) and Vulgan (Team Spirit, Foinavon, Gay Trip) **pic**: Rough Quest

Page 23 – ODDITIES

a. Butter **b**. Jumped every fence on the National course (minus horse) **c**. 15.2 hands **d.** 17 years

Page 25 – FENCES

a. The Chair (5ft 2in fence with 6ft ditch) **b**. Captain Becher fell off Conrad into the brook during the first National **c**. 4ft 10in (and a 5ft 6in brook with a drop) **d.** After the 1989 race

Page 27 – WINNERS

a. Ben Nevis **b**. The race was void after two false starts **c**. L'Escargot **d.** A hotel bus

Page 29 – GEOGRAPHY

a. Liverpool **b**. Leeds-Liverpool Canal **c.** Melling **d.** L9

Page 31 – TELEVISION

a. *Champions* **b**. 1960 **c.** Peter O'Sullevan **d.** 1997

Page 33 – RED RUM

a. 1973 **b.** The sands of Southport beach **c**. Crisp **d.** 1975, 1976

Page 35 – TRAINERS

a. Jenny Pitman **b**. Ginger McCain **c**. Ted and Ruby Walsh (Papillon) **d.** Frank Gilman (Grittar)

Page 37 – ROYALTY

a. Devon Loch **b**. The Scot **c.** The Prince of Wales became King Edward VII **d.** Fifth **pic**: Royal Athlete

Page 38 – SENSATION

a. Cancer **b.** A broken hock bone **c.** Churchtown Boy by 25 lengths **d.** Captain Martin Becher

Page 39 – SENSATION

a. A second false start was not clearly signalled and the race could not be re-run **b**. Seven **c.** Esha Ness **d.** Richard Dunwoody

Page 43 – OWNERS

a. Fred Pontin **b**. Nick Embiricos **c**. Gregory Peck **d.** Noel le Mare **pic**: Last Suspect

Page 45 – WINNERS

a. Eye **b**. Seven **c.** 1934 **d.** Cheltenham Gold Cup **pic**: Nigel Hawke

Page 47 – FILMS

a. *National Velvet* **b**. Bob Champion and Aldaniti **c**. John Hurt **d.** John Irvin **pic**: Aldaniti

Page 49 – LIVERPOOL

a. George Stubbs **b**. Elizabeth I's (over Kirkdale Sands) **c**. The Derby (named after the Earl of Derby in 1780) **d.** Stanley Racing

Page 50 – JOCKEYS

a. Mr Marcus Armytage **b.** They both came second (Richard on Crisp, Mark on Garrison Savannah **c.** Richard Dunwoody **d.** Dick Francis

Page 51 – JOCKEYS

a. Richard Guest **b**. Tony Dobbin **c.** Geraldine Rees (1982) **d.** Beasley

Page 53 – RACE DAYS

a. May **b**. 1947 **c**. 1992 **d.** Six

Page 55 – AINTREE

a. An American Army base **b**. The second Earl of Sefton **c**. Lord Daresbury **d.** Gatwick, West Sussex

Page 57 – TRAINERS

a. Martin Pipe **b.** Three (Early Mist, Royal Tan, Quare Times) **c.** Aldaniti **d.** Donald

Page 59 – SENSATION

a. He had his injured arm strapped to his side **b.** Canal Turn **c.** Number 23 (Foinavon) **d.** Canal Turn

Page 61 – THE COURSE

a. 30 (16 on the first circuit, 14 on the second) **b.** The Chair and the Water Jump **c.** Four and a half miles (4 miles 856 yards) **d.** The Elbow

Page 62 – FENCES

a. Foinavon **b.** The 90° turn immediately after the fence **c.** The Melling Road **d.** The Water Jump

Page 63 – FENCES

a. False (he came third) **b.** 4ft 6in **c.** Spruce **d.** Number 14

Page 65 – RED RUM

a. Two **b.** 1995 **c.** 30 years **d.** By the winning post at Aintree **pic**: Philip Blacker

Page 67 – WINNERS

a. Red Rum (in 1974 Liverpool switched from Lancashire to Merseyside) **b.** Lottery **c.** Wild Man of Borneo (1895) **d.** ESB (1956) and Oxo (1959) **pic**: 7-1

Page 69 – WATCHING

a. Princess Royal Stand **b.** Queen Mother Stand **c.** The Chair **d.** West Tip Seats, Aldaniti Stand **pic**: Happy Valley, Hong Kong

Page 71 -- SPEED
a. Mr Frisk **b**. Abd-El-Kader (1850) **c.** 8 mins 47.8 secs **d.** 9 mins 20.2 secs **pic**: Mr Marcus Armytage
Page 73 – PRIZES
a. Three horses landing over Becher's **b**. £500,000 **c**. Boodle & Dunthorne **d.** £2,000 **pic**: Becher's
Page 77 – RED RUM
a. Southport **b.** 1974 **c.** Brian Fletcher, Tommy Stack **d.** Andy Pandy
Page 79 – SENSATION
a. A horse (Zoedone) was severely poisoned **b**. Monday **c**. A bomb scare **d.** 70,000 **pic**: The horses
Page 81 – SPONSORS
a. The winning horse was called Seagram **b.** Martell **c.** 1715 **d.** The News of the World **pic**: Oak
Page 83 – WINNERS
a. Aldaniti **b**. Reynoldstown **c**. Poethlyn (Gatwick 1918, Aintree 1919) **d.** Three (- Alligator, - Rum, - Marauder) **pic**: Ruby Walsh on Papillon
Page 85 – OWNERS
a. The Summit Partnership (1998) **b**. Raymond Mould **c.** James Machell (1873, 1874, 1876) **d.** The Prince of Wales, (later Edward VII)
Page 87 – TELEVISION
a. 1927 **b**. 2001 **c**. 120 countries **d.** Over half a billion
pic: Sir Peter O'Sullevan

Page 88 – RACING RULES

a. A handicap steeplechase **b.** Six or over **c**. The Pardubice
d. Gerry Scott (1960 on Merriman II, and 1996)

Page 89 – RACING RULES

a. By raising the tape **b.** 1843 **c**. Manifesto **d.** 9-6

Page 93 – RACE DAYS

a. 100,000 **b**. Happy Valley, Hong Kong **c**. 50,000 **d.** 1987

Page 95 – WINNERS

a. She was the first mare to win **b**. He was a grey **c**. Manifesto
d. University of Liverpool **pic**: Three

Page 97 – SENSATION

a. Seven **b**. Devon Loch **c**. Cure-All **d.** He rode without stirrups from Fence 22 onwards

Page 99 – JOCKEYS

a. John White **b**. None (he was a flat race jockey) **c**. Poethlyn (twice) and Jerry M **d.** Five (between 1856-1870) **pic**: 2002

Page 101 – FILMS

a. Elizabeth Taylor **b.** The Pie **c**. She won, but was disqualified for being a girl **d.** Tatum O'Neal

Page 103 – WINNERS

a. Voluptuary (1884) **b**. A tube in his neck to help him breathe
c. Nicolaus Silver (1961) **d.** The Colonel

Page 105 – 2003

a. Papillon, Red Marauder, Bindaree **b**. 149 **c.** Thursday 3rd April
d. Saturday 5th April, 3.45pm

LIVERPOOL
the first 1,000 years

by Arabella McIntyre-Brown
and Guy Woodland
ISBN 1-904099-00-9
240pp, 250 colour photos
'a must-have book for anyone who loves Liverpool'

CROSS THE MERSEY - 850 YEARS OF THE FAMOUS MERSEY FERRIES

by Arabella McIntyre-Brown
and Guy Woodland
ISBN 1-904099-03-3
112pp, 120 colour photos
'a total ferries experience exploring the ferries, the Mersey and the environment'

Christmas Day Liverpool Quiz Book

by Arabella McIntyre-Brown
and Guy Woodland
ISBN 1-904099-02-5
How much do you know about Liverpool? Test your knowledge!

For details of how to buy: **www.garlicpress.co.uk**